A BARTIMAEUS GRAPHIC NOVEL

...t of

Samarkand

BASED ON THE NOVEL BY

AND ...

ART BY
LEE SULLIVAN

COLOUR BY
NICOLAS CHAPUIS

LETTERING BY
CHRIS DICKEY

CORGI BOOKS

WITHDRAWN

THE AMULET OF SAMARKAND: A BARTIMAEUS GRAPHIC NOVEL
A CORGI BOOK 978 0 552 56370 3

First published by Disney • Hyperion Books, 2010
First published in Great Britain by Corgi,
An imprint of Random House Children's Books
A Random House Group Company

Adapted from *The Amulet of Samarkand*, first published by Doubleday,
an imprint of Random House Children's Books, 2003

This edition published 2011

1 3 5 7 9 10 8 6 4 2

Text copyright © Jonathan Stroud, 2010
Illustrations copyright © Lee Sullivan, 2010

The Random House Group Limited supports the Forest Stewardship Council (FSC),
the leading international forest certification organization. All our titles that are printed on
Greenpeace-approved FSC-certified paper carry the FSC logo. Our paper procurement
policy can be found at www.rbooks.co.uk/environment.

Corgi Books are published by Random House Children's Books,
61-63 Uxbridge Road, London W5 5SA

www.**kidsatrandomhouse**.co.uk
www.**rbooks**.co.uk

Addresses for companies within The Random House Group Limited can be found at:
www.randomhouse.co.uk/offices.htm

THE RANDOM HOUSE GROUP Limited Reg. No. 954009

A CIP catalogue record for this book is available from the British Library.

Printed in China

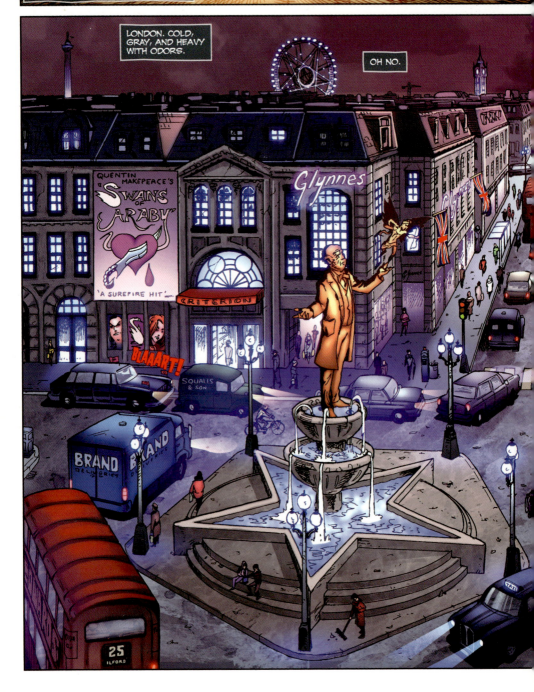

AS ALWAYS, OF COURSE, I TRIED TO RESIST.

I TRIED TO COUNTERACT THE PULL, BUT THE WRENCHING WORDS WERE JUST TOO STRONG. EACH SYLLABLE WAS A HARPOON SPEARING MY SUBSTANCE, DRAGGING ME OFF.

FOR THREE SHORT SECONDS, THE GENTLE GRAVITY OF THE OTHER PLACE HELPED HOLD ME BACK...THEN, ALL AT ONCE, I WAS EXPELLED OUT INTO THE WORLD...

LONDON. COLD, GRAY, AND HEAVY WITH ODORS.

OH NO.

QUENTIN MAKEPEACE'S "SWANS OF ARABY"

'A SUREFIRE HIT'.

CRITERION

Glynnes

BLAAART!

SQUALLS & SON

BRAND DELIVERIES

25 ILFORD

AAARKK!

EVENING EDITION. LATEST NEWS!

AAARKK!

CHAPTER I

BARTIMAEUS

THE TEMPERATURE OF THE ROOM DROPPED FAST. ICE FORMED ON THE CURTAINS AND CANDLES.

KRRACKLE

THE ROOM FILLED WITH A YELLOW, CHOKING CLOUD OF BRIMSTONE.

INDISTINCT BLACK SHADOWS WRITHED AND ROILED INSIDE IT.

THE CLOUD FORMED TENDRILS THAT LICKED THE AIR LIKE HUNGRY TONGUES.

SCHLUURPP

SCHLUURPP

INVISIBLE FEET PATTERED ACROSS FLOORBOARDS, AND INVISIBLE MOUTHS WHISPERED WICKED THINGS FROM BEHIND THE BED AND UNDER THE DESK.

THUB
THUB THUB

FROM FAR AWAY CAME THE SOUND OF MANY VOICES SCREAMING...

AAAIIEEE!

HEY, IT WAS HIS FIRST TIME.

I WANTED TO SCARE HIM.

FZZZT

FZZZT

FZZZT

I DID, TOO.

I CHARGE YOU... TO...TO T-T-TELL ME YOUR NAME.

HE KNEW AND I KNEW THAT HE KNEW MY NAME ALREADY.

I AM BARTIMAEUS.

OTHERWISE, HOW COULD HE HAVE SUMMONED ME IN THE FIRST PLACE? YOU NEED THE RIGHT WORDS, THE RIGHT ACTIONS, AND MOST OF ALL, THE RIGHT NAME.

I SAW HIM GIVE A GULP. GOOD, HE KNEW MY REPUTATION.

ARE YOU THAT BARTIMAEUS WHO IN OLDEN TIMES WAS SUMMONED BY THE MAGICIANS TO REPAIR THE WALLS OF PRAGUE AND WHO DID—

WHAT A TIME WASTER THIS KID WAS.

I UPPED THE VOLUME A BIT ON THIS ONE.

I AM BARTIMAEUS! I AM SAKHR AL-JINNI, N'GORSO THE MIGHTY, AND SERPENT OF SILVER PLUMES! I HAVE REBUILT THE WALLS OF URUK, KARNAK, AND PRAGUE. I HAVE SPOKEN WITH SOLOMON. I HAVE WATCHED OVER OLD ZIMBABWE TILL THE STONES FELL AND THE JACKALS FED ON ITS PEOPLE.

I AM BARTIMAEUS! I RECOGNIZE NO MASTER! SO I CHARGE YOU, *BOY*. WHO ARE YOU TO SUMMON ME?

IMPRESSIVE STUFF, EH? ALL TRUE AS WELL, WHICH GAVE IT EVEN MORE POWER.

I RATHER HOPED HE WOULD BE BLUSTERED INTO TELLING ME HIS NAME OR STEPPING OUTSIDE THE CIRCLE SO I COULD NAB HIM.

NO LUCK THERE, THEN.

BY THE CONSTRAINTS OF THE CIRCLE, THE POINTS ON THE PENTACLE, AND THE CHAIN OF RUNES, I AM YOUR MASTER!

YOU WILL OBEY ME!

I MUST ADMIT I WAS ALREADY SURPRISED. YOU DON'T OFTEN GET SMALL ONES LIKE THIS SQUIRT CALLING UP AN EXTRAORDINARILY POWERFUL AND MODEST ENTITY LIKE MYSELF.

ANYTHING TO GET THIS OVER WITH QUICKLY.

WHAT IS YOUR WILL?

I WAITED GRIMLY FOR THE PATHETIC REQUEST. LEVITATING SOME TATTY OBJECT WAS A USUAL ONE. OR MOVING IT AROUND THE ROOM A BIT.

PERHAPS HE'D WANT ME TO CONJURE AN ILLUSION. THAT MIGHT BE FUN. THERE WAS BOUND TO BE A WAY OF MISINTERPRETING HIS REQUEST.

ONCE, A MAGICIAN DEMANDED I SHOW HIM THE LOVE OF HIS LIFE. I RUSTLED UP A MIRROR.

WELL, BOY?

I CHARGE YOU TO RETRIEVE THE AMULET OF SAMARKAND FROM THE HOUSE OF SIMON LOVELACE AND BRING IT TO ME WHEN I SUMMON YOU AT DAWN TOMORROW.

IT WAS PEEING WITH NOVEMBER RAIN.

JUST MY LUCK.

I HAD TAKEN THE FORM OF A BLACKBIRD, AND WITHIN SECONDS I WAS AS BEDRAGGLED A FOWL AS EVER HUNCHED ITS WINGS IN HAMPSTEAD.

THE VILLAS OPPOSITE LOOKED LIKE THE FACES OF THE DEAD. OR PERHAPS IT WAS JUST MY MOOD.

CHAPTER 2

BARTIMAEUS

FIVE THINGS WERE BOTHERING ME.

FOR A START, THE DULL ACHE THAT COMES WITH EVERY PHYSICAL MANIFESTATION WAS ALREADY BEGINNING. I COULD FEEL IT IN MY FEATHERS.

THE SECOND THING WAS THE WEATHER.

ENOUGH SAID.

THIRD, I'D FORGOTTEN THE LIMITATIONS OF MATERIAL BODIES. I HAD AN ITCH JUST ABOVE MY BEAK THAT I COULDN'T REACH TO SCRATCH.

FOURTH, THAT KID.

WHO WAS HE, AND WHY DID HE HAVE A DEATH WISH?

FIFTH...THE AMULET. WHAT THE KID THOUGHT HE WAS GOING TO DO WITH IT WAS ANYONE'S GUESS.

I HAD TO STEAL IT FIRST, THOUGH, AND THAT WOULD NOT NECESSARILY BE EASY, EVEN FOR ME.

CHAPTER 3

BARTIMAEUS

THE TASTE OF MUD IS NO FIT THING FOR A BEING OF AIR AND FIRE.

BUT THERE'S NO POINT BEING FASTIDIOUS WHEN YOU HAVE A PROTECTIVE SHIELD TO BYPASS.

I AM CHOOSY ABOUT MY INCARNATIONS.

BIRDS, GOOD. INSECTS, GOOD. BATS, OKAY. THINGS THAT RUN FAST ARE FINE. TREE DWELLERS ARE EVEN BETTER. SUBTERRANEAN THINGS, NOT GOOD.

MOLES, BAD.

IT WILL BE THE MOST MAGNIFICENT OCCASION, AMANDA. YOU WILL BE THE TOAST OF LONDON SOCIETY...

WITH SOME RELIEF, I BECAME A FLY.

TWO HUMANS WERE SITTING UNDERNEATH A HIDEOUS CRYSTAL THING THAT WAS PRETENDING TO BE A CHANDELIER.

AND YOU'RE SURE THE PRIME MINISTER WILL COME?

AMANDA, HE IS VERY MUCH LOOKING FORWARD TO VIEWING YOUR ESTATE.

I MEMORIZED THE WOMAN INSTANTLY. I WOULD APPEAR IN HER GUISE TOMORROW WHEN I WENT BACK TO VISIT THAT KID. ONLY NAKED. LET'S SEE HOW HIS ADOLESCENT MIND COPED WITH THAT.

CHAPTER 4

BARTIMAEUS

ON THE SECOND PLANE, I SAW AN IMP FLOATING OVER LOVELACE'S SHOULDER ON THE LOOKOUT FOR DANGER.

EVEN WITH YOUR MANY RIVALS HOUNDING HIM THESE LAST FEW WEEKS?

DESPITE THEIR CONSTANT EFFORTS TO HAVE IT MOVED, HE HAS REMAINED COMMITTED TO HOLDING THE CONFERENCE AT YOUR DELIGHTFUL HALL.

YOU'VE ALWAYS KNOWN HOW TO PLAY THE P.M., SIMON. HOW TO FLATTER HIS VANITY.

IT WAS A PITY I WASN'T A SPIDER. THEY CAN SIT FOR HOURS.

FLIES ARE MORE JITTERY, AND I HAD TO FORCE MY UNWILLING BODY TO LURK.

KEEP IT TO YOURSELF, MY LOVE, BUT ALL HE REALLY HAS LEFT NOW IS CHARM, AND MOST DAYS HE DOESN'T EVEN BOTHER WITH THAT.

PARDON ME SIR, BUT THE CARS ARE READY.

IT PAINS ME, AMANDA, BUT DUTY CALLS. I MUST RETURN TO PARLIAMENT.

MY GOOD FRIEND, MAKEPEACE, HAS SENT THE TICKETS FOR HIS PLAY, SO I SHALL SEE YOU AT THE THEATER TOMORROW EVENING.

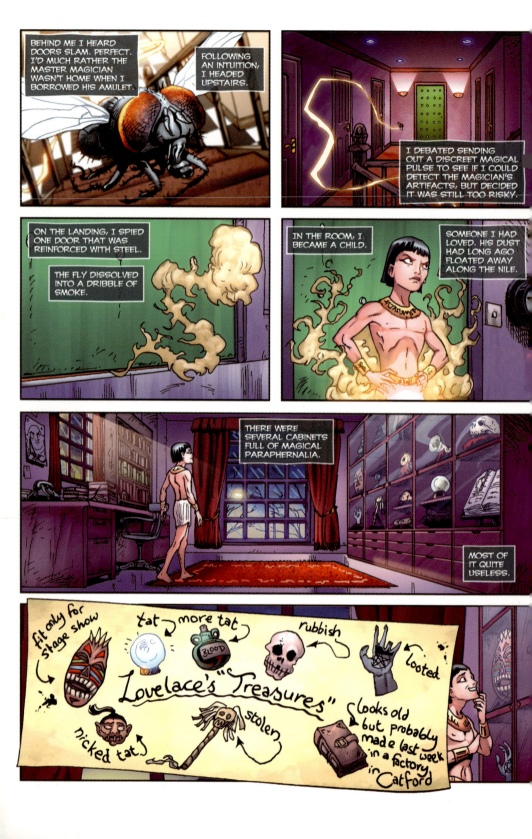

BEHIND ME I HEARD DOORS SLAM. PERFECT. I'D MUCH RATHER THE MASTER MAGICIAN WASN'T HOME WHEN I BORROWED HIS AMULET.

FOLLOWING AN INTUITION, I HEADED UPSTAIRS.

I DEBATED SENDING OUT A DISCREET MAGICAL PULSE TO SEE IF I COULD DETECT THE MAGICIAN'S ARTIFACTS, BUT DECIDED IT WAS STILL TOO RISKY.

ON THE LANDING, I SPIED ONE DOOR THAT WAS REINFORCED WITH STEEL.

THE FLY DISSOLVED INTO A DRIBBLE OF SMOKE.

IN THE ROOM, I BECAME A CHILD.

SOMEONE I HAD LOVED. HIS DUST HAD LONG AGO FLOATED AWAY ALONG THE NILE.

THERE WERE SEVERAL CABINETS FULL OF MAGICAL PARAPHERNALIA.

MOST OF IT QUITE USELESS.

fit only for stage show

tat → more tat

rubbish

looted

Lovelace's "Treasures"

BLOOD

stolen

nicked tat

looks old but probably made last week in a factory in Catford

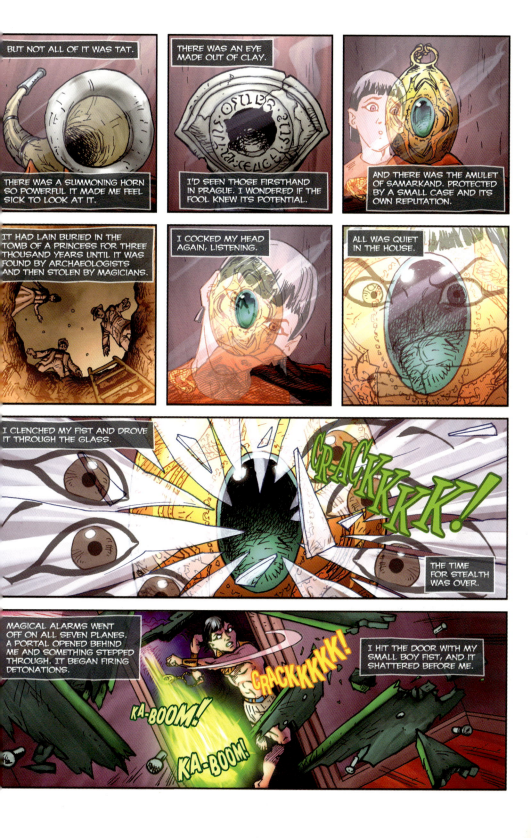

FOOM!

FOOM!

I HAD TO GET OUT OF THE HOUSE, AND FAST.

I RAN THROUGH SEVERAL ROOMS, EACH TIME MAKING A BREAK FOR THE WINDOW...

...AND EACH TIME RETREATING WHEN ONE OR MORE OF THE SENTRIES APPEARED.

KA-BOOM!

KA-BOOM!

I FOUND MYSELF IN THE KITCHEN, AND WITH GROWING FRUSTRATION SAW THE THREE SENTINELS APPEAR AGAIN. I PUT A SEAL ON THE DOOR TO STOP WHATEVER WAS CHASING ME AND TO BUY SOME TIME.

HELLO... BARTIMAEUS.

STILL RUNNING AWAY FROM JABOR, EH?

I FELT A SLIGHT UNEASE.

I CHECKED OUT THE COOK. ON PLANES ONE TO SIX HE WAS THE SAME, BUT ON THE SEVENTH PLANE...UH-OH...TENTACLES.

HELLO, FAQUARL.

HOW'S IT GOING?

NOT BAD.

HAVEN'T SEEN YOU AROUND.

NO, GUESS NOT.

THE AMULET ITSELF WOULD PROTECT ME FROM MAGICAL ATTACKS BUT NOT FROM FAQUARL'S MORE PHYSICAL TALENTS. I PLAYED FOR TIME. AGAIN.

IF YOU AND JABOR ARE HIS SLAVES, THEN THIS LOVELACE MUST BE FAIRLY POTENT.

NOW, NOW, BARTIMAEUS, WE DON'T USE THE WORD "SLAVES" IN CIVILIZED COMPANY, DO WE? JABOR AND I ARE PLAYING THE LONG GAME.

AND I'M GOING TO HAVE TO ASK YOU TO TAKE OFF A CERTAIN AMULET AND PUT IT ON THE TABLE.

I WAS TRAPPED. BEHIND MY SEAL, JABOR'S PATIENT (IF UNIMAGINATIVE) DETONATIONS STILL SOUNDED. THE DOOR ITSELF MUST HAVE LONG SINCE BEEN TURNED TO POWDER. BY THE WINDOW, THE THREE SENTINELS HOVERED.

THAT'S KIND OF YOU, BUT YOU KNOW I CAN'T DO THAT.

YOU CAN AND YOU WILL. IT IS NOTHING PERSONAL, OF COURSE. ONE DAY WE MIGHT WORK TOGETHER AGAIN. BUT FOR NOW, I TOO HAVE A CHARGE TO FULFILL.

KA-BOOM!

KA-BOOM!

I LOOKED AROUND THE ROOM FOR INSPIRATION.

I LEAPT AND AT THE EXACT SAME MOMENT RELEASED THE SEAL ON THE DOORWAY. A PARTICULARLY POWERFUL DETONATION CAME SHOOTING THROUGH THE EMPTY GAP.

KA-BOOM!

SADLY, THE BLAST CAUGHT FAQUARL SQUARE ON AND BLASTED HIM BACK INTO THE FRIDGE. BOO HOO.

I BROKE OUT INTO THE GARDEN AND CAST AN ILLUMINATION OF THE BRIGHTEST KIND. THE GARDEN LIT UP AS IF BY AN EXPLODING SUN.

I LEAPT OVER THE BLINDED SENTRIES, AND THEN VAULTED THE WALL.

BY THE TIME FAQUARL AND JABOR MADE IT TO THE STREET, I WAS NOWHERE TO BE SEEN.

I WAS LONG GONE.

HIGHGATE, NORTH LONDON.

BEFORE.

"Above all, there is one fact that we must drive into your wretched little skull now so that you never forget it."

"Yes, sir."

"Do you know what that fact is?"

"No, sir."

"No? Well then, boy, I shall tell you. It is this. Demons are very, very wicked. They will hurt you if they can. Do you understand?"

"Yes, sir."

I cannot stop watching his eyebrows.

ARE YOU SURE, BOY?

YES, SIR. I UNDERSTAND. DEMONS ARE VERY, VERY WICKED AND WILL HURT YOU IF THEY CAN.

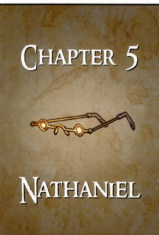

CHAPTER 5

NATHANIEL

WELL NOW, YOU SAY YES, AND I AM SURE YOU MEAN YES — AND YET...

I DO NOT FEEL CONVINCED THAT YOU REALLY, TRULY UNDERSTAND.

"Go to my study, boy. On my desk is a box. In the box is a pair of spectacles. Put them on and come back to me. Simple, yes?"

I had never been allowed in this room before.

STOP! B-... BEGONE!

Then I remembered the spectacles.

CHAPTER 6

BARTIMAEUS

I FLEW FROM HAMPSTEAD AT TOP SPEED AND TOOK SHELTER UNDER THE EAVES OF A DESERTED HOUSE BY THE THAMES.

I PREENED MY FEATHERS AND WATCHED THE SKY.

AS I EXPECTED, THE MAGICIAN SENT OUT SEARCH SPHERES TO HUNT DOWN HIS AMULET.

ONE OF THE PROBLEMS WITH POWERFUL, MAGICAL ARTIFACTS IS THAT THEY HAVE A DISTINCTIVE PULSATING AURA THAT'S ABOUT AS SUBTLE AS A NAKED MAN AT A FUNERAL.

I KNEW I HAD TO KEEP MOVING.

SO I CONTINUED MY FRANTIC, FUGITIVE DANCE ACROSS LONDON. THE URCHIN HAD FORBIDDEN ME TO RETURN BEFORE DAWN AND I WOULD BE EXHAUSTED LONG BEFORE THAT.

LONDON

I DECIDED ON A NEW PLAN. I WOULD DROWN OUT THE AMULET'S PULSE BY MINGLING WITH THE GREAT UNWASHED — IN OTHER WORDS, WITH PEOPLE.

I WAS THAT DESPERATE.

CHAPTER 7

BARTIMAEUS

THE OLD PAIN HAD STARTED UP AGAIN, THROBBING IN MY STOMACH AND THROUGH MY BONES. IT WASN'T HEALTHY TO BE ENCASED IN A PHYSICAL BODY FOR SO LONG.

THE AMULET BEAT AGAINST MY CHEST WITH EVERY STEP. I WOULD HAVE HAPPILY LOBBED IT INTO THE NEAREST TRASH CAN, BUT I WAS BOUND BY MY ORDERS FROM THAT KID.

THE MASSED DARKNESS OF THE HIGH BUILDINGS CLOSED IN ON EITHER SIDE, OPPRESSING ME.

CITIES GET ME DOWN, ALMOST AS IF I WERE UNDERGROUND.

THEY MAKE ME LONG FOR THE SOUTH.

IT WOULD HAVE BEEN A LOT MORE AGREEABLE TO RETURN TO THE URCHIN IMMEDIATELY TO RID MYSELF OF THE AMULET.

BUT MAGICIANS ALMOST ALWAYS INSIST ON SUMMONING US AT SPECIFIC TIMES. IT REMOVES THE POSSIBILITY OF OUR CATCHING THEM AT A (POTENTIALLY FATAL) DISADVANTAGE.

THE BOY WOULD PAY FOR THIS. YOU DIDN'T REDUCE BARTIMAEUS OF URUK TO DOSSING IN DOORWAYS AND GET AWAY WITH IT.

THEN I HEARD SOMETHING. FOOTSTEPS IN THE ALLEY.

IT WAS THE CHILDREN FROM TRAFALGAR SQUARE WITH THE GIRL AT THEIR HEAD.

I CAST A SOPHISTICATED CONCEALMENT UPON MYSELF.

A LAYER OF TIGHTLY LACED PURPLE THREADS COVERED ME, RENDING ME UTTERLY INVISIBLE.

IT'S THERE.

GET IT.

OOPS.

I WAS OVERWHELMED BY A TIDAL WAVE OF DISTRESSED LEATHER, CHEAP AFTERSHAVE, AND BODY ODOR.

BUT I AM BARTIMAEUS, AND I LET LOOSE A BRIEF DISCHARGE OF HEAT AND LIGHT THAT SHOULD HAVE REDUCED THE BOYS TO CHARRED CORPSES...

...BUT SOMEHOW DIDN'T. MY MAGIC SEEMED NOT TO AFFECT THESE CHILDREN AT ALL.

YOU HAVE SOMETHING AROUND YOUR NECK.

SAYS WHO?

IT'S BEEN IN FULL VIEW FOR THE LAST TWO MINUTES, YOU CRETIN.

OH. FAIR ENOUGH.

YOU'RE NOT A MAGICIAN.

TOO RIGHT, I'M NOT! WOULD A MAGICIAN DO SO WELL AGAINST YOUR WICKEDNESS?

SHE HAD A POINT THERE. EVEN WITH A DOZEN CHARMS, AN ARMY OF IMPS, AND A HEAVYWEIGHT DJINNI, A MAGICIAN WOULD HAVE HAD A JOB SUBDUING THE GREAT BARTIMAEUS.

THIS GIRL AND HER BOYFRIENDS HAD DONE IT ALL ON THEIR OWN, WITHOUT SEEMING PARTICULARLY FUSSED.

CHAPTER 8

NATHANIEL

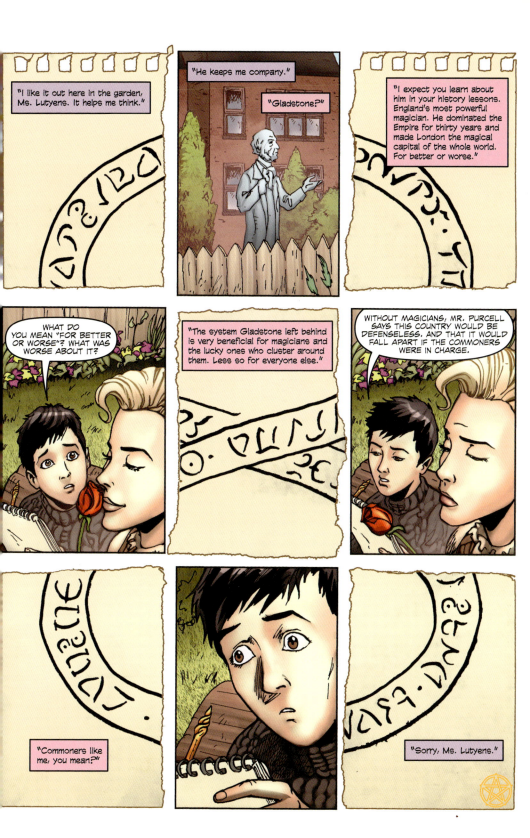

Chapter 9

Bartimaeus

IN THE END, DAWN CAME.

THE WHOLE OF THE NIGHT HAD BEEN WEARISOME AND I WAITED IMPATIENTLY FOR THE SUMMONS.

I WAS NOW ON THE ROOF OF WESTMINSTER ABBEY PRETENDING TO BE A GARGOYLE. THINGS DON'T GET MUCH WORSE THAN THAT.

I ALLOWED MYSELF A SHORT, LUXURIOUS FLEX OF MY WINGS.

AND AT THAT MOMENT, THE SUMMONS CAME. A THOUSAND PAINFUL FISHHOOKS SEEMED TO EMBED THEMSELVES IN ME.

I SUBMITTED IMMEDIATELY. I WISHED ONLY TO HAND OVER THE AMULET...

...AND BE DONE.

I ORDER YOU, BARTIMAEUS, TO REVEAL WHETHER YOU HAVE DILIGENTLY AND--

OF COURSE I HAVE - WHAT DO YOU THINK THIS IS?

IT WAS SIMON LOVELACE'S. NOW IT IS YOURS. SOON IT WILL BE SIMON LOVELACE'S AGAIN.

TAKE IT AND ENJOY THE CONSEQUENCES.

I MADE A BIG SHOW OF CHECKING THE LINES OF THE CIRCLE.

AHA! YOU'VE SPELLED THIS WRONG! AND YOU KNOW WHAT THAT MEANS!

THE KID'S FACE WENT AN INTERESTING MIX OF WHITE AND RED AS HE STUDIED THE LINES HIMSELF.

RECREANT DEMON! THE PENTACLE IS SOUND — IT BINDS YOU STILL!

OKAY, I LIED. NOW DO YOU WANT THIS OR NOT?

I WATCHED HIM CLOSELY. IF ONE FOOT OR ONE FINGER FELL OUTSIDE THE CIRCLE, I WOULD BE ON HIM FASTER THAN A PRAYING MANTIS. SADLY, HE PRODUCED A STICK.

EUCH, THIS IS DISGUSTING!

BLAME ROTHERHITHE SEWAGE WORKS AND THE DEMONIC HORDES OF LONDON THAT WERE CHASING ME.

YOU WERE PURSUED?

YOU SOUND ALMOST PLEASED. WRONG EMOTION, KID. TRY FEAR.

WELL, NO MATTER. I HAVE CARRIED OUT MY CHARGE. MY TASK IS DONE. FOR THE REMAINDER OF YOUR SHORT LIFE, FAREWELL!

YOU CANNOT DEPART! I HAVE OTHER WORK FOR THEE. ADELBRAND'S PENTACLE HOLDS YOU AT MY COMMAND.

MORE THAN THE RENEWED CAPTIVITY, IT WAS THE OCCASIONAL ARCHAISMS THAT ANNOYED ME SO MUCH. I ASK YOU... "THEE" AND "RECREANT DEMON"?!

BARTIMAEUS, I CHARGE YOU TO TAKE THE AMULET OF SAMARKAND AND HIDE IT IN THE MAGICAL REPOSITORY OF THE MAGICIAN ARTHUR UNDERWOOD, CONCEALING IT SO THAT HE CANNOT OBSERVE IT.

THEN YOU ARE TO RETURN TO ME IMMEDIATELY TO AWAIT FURTHER INSTRUCTIONS.

VERY WELL. WHERE DOES THIS UNFORTUNATE MAGICIAN RESIDE?

DOWNSTAIRS.

OUCH.

Chapter 10
Bartimaeus

DOWNSTAIRS? NOW THAT IS NASTY.

I JUST WANT IT SAFE. NO ONE'LL FIND IT THERE.

BUT IF THEY DO, YOU'RE IN THE CLEAR. TYPICAL MAGICIAN'S TRICK.

NO ONE'S GOING TO FIND IT.

YOU THINK NOT. WE'LL SEE.

FRAMING ANOTHER MAGICIAN WASN'T UNUSUAL.

MAGICIANS ARE THE MOST CONNIVING, JEALOUS, DUPLICITOUS GROUP OF PEOPLE ON EARTH, EVEN INCLUDING LAWYERS.

FRAMING YOUR OWN MASTER, THOUGH, NOW THAT *WAS* OUT OF THE ORDINARY.

I ENCASED THE AMULET WITH A CHARM, GIVING IT THE APPEARANCE OF A DRIFTING COBWEB.

THEN, IN SPIDER GUISE, I CRAWLED CAUTIOUSLY DOWN THROUGH THE CRACKS IN THE HOUSE.

AFTER SEVERAL MINUTES OF SCUTTLING, I FOUND THE STUDY.

THE SIMPLE TRAP AT THE ENTRANCE MIGHT HAVE SEEN OFF A CURIOUS HOUSEMAID, BUT NOT BARTIMAEUS.

THE AMULET DID ITS JOB AND ABSORBED THE BLAST.

IF THE BOY THOUGHT THE AMULET WOULD BE SAFE BEHIND HIS MASTER'S "SECURITY," HE HAD ANOTHER THINK COMING.

A PITIFUL ARRAY OF MAGICAL GIMCRACKS HAD BEEN ARRANGED HERE WITH SADLY LOVING CARE.

I ALMOST FELT SORRY FOR THE UNSUSPECTING DUFFER AS I PULLED THE COBWEB OVER A FAKE LUCKY RABBIT'S FOOT.

I WAS HEADING UP TO THE ATTIC ROOM AGAIN... WHEN THINGS GOT RATHER INTERESTING.

THE BOY WAS HEADING DOWNSTAIRS, TRAILING IN THE WAKE OF THE MAGICIAN'S WIFE.

HE LOOKED THOROUGHLY FED UP.

THIS WAS BAD. HE HAD LOST CONTROL OF THE SITUATION, A DANGEROUS THING FOR ANY MAGICIAN.

HE'S IN THERE. GO STRAIGHT IN...

...NATHANIEL.

THE SPIDER REMAINED MOTIONLESS. BUT INWARDLY IT WAS THRILLED.

I HAD HIS NAME!

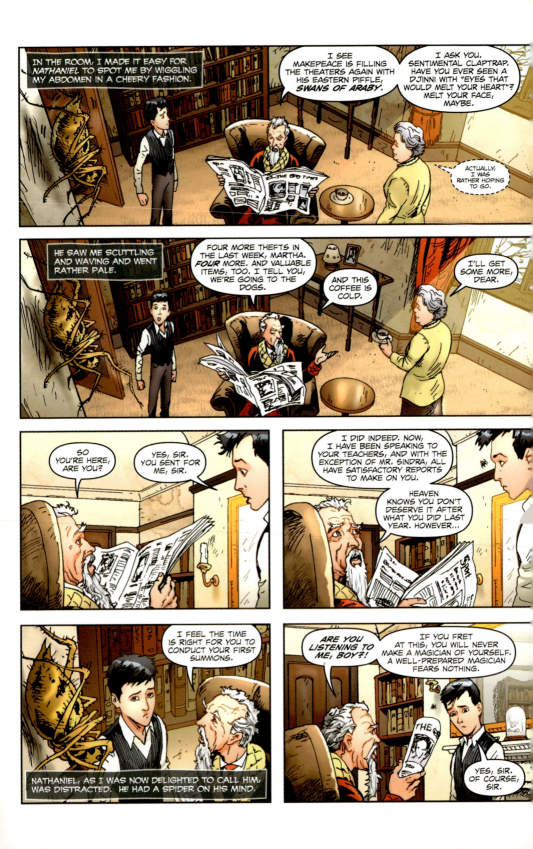

CHAPTER II

NATHANIEL

BEFORE.

THE DAY EVERYTHING CHANGED.

"Quickly, Nathaniel. The master wants to present you."

THIS IS THE BOY.

DO YOU BEAT HIM?

RARELY.

I'LL BET HE EATS LIKE A FERRET, TOO.

GREEDY, IS HE?

YES, SOME BOYS ARE.

LET'S SEE WHAT YOU'VE TAUGHT THIS WHIPPET OF YOURS, SHALL WE, UNDERWOOD?

IT'LL BE AMUSING.

HOW MANY CLASSIFIED TYPES OF SPIRIT ARE THERE?

THIRTEEN THOUSAND AND FORTY-SIX, SIR.

AND UNCLASSIFIED?

PETRONIUS POSTULATES FORTY-FIVE THOUSAND, SIR.

WHAT IS THE MODUS OPERANDI OF THE CARTHAGINIAN SUBGROUP?

THEY APPEAR AS CRYING INFANTS, SIR.

WHAT ARE THE SIX WORDS OF DIRECTION? ANY LANGUAGE.

APPARE; MANE; AUSCULTA; SE DEDE; PARE; REDI: APPEAR; REMAIN; LISTEN; SUBMIT; OBEY; RETURN.

BE FAIR, SIMON, HE CAN'T KNOW THAT YET!

BRAVO.

STANDARDS MUST HAVE DROPPED IF A BACKWARD APPRENTICE CAN BE CONGRATULATED FOR SPOUTING SOMETHING WE ALL LEARNED AT OUR MOTHERS' TEATS.

YOU'RE...

...YOU'RE JUST A SORE LOSER.

YOU COCKSURE GUTTERSNIPE. YOU'RE HELPLESS. YOU KNOW A FEW WORDS, BUT YOU'RE CAPABLE OF NOTHING.

GET OUT OF MY SIGHT.

LEAVE US, BOY.

"You're helpless."

"You're capable of nothing."

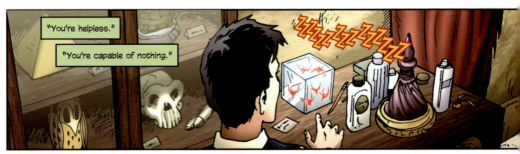

"You're helpless."

"You're capable of nothing."

ZZZZ ZZZZ
ZZ ZZZ

PHZZZ

WHAT THE—

HOW DID YOU GET ON AT THE PARTY? IT SOUNDED QUITE A BOISTEROUS AFFAIR.

YOU LOOK ILL. YOU'RE SHAKING! ARE YOU ALL RIGHT?

CRACCCKKKKKKKKKK!

"Now you really *will* learn something, lad."

It is a long, wet autumn.

CHAPTER 12

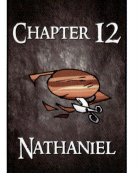

NATHANIEL

I make swift progress with my studies for my mind is full of hate.

GLADSTONE DID MORE THAN ANYONE ELSE TO HELP LONDON ASCEND TO MAGICAL PROMINENCE. SOON, LONDON OVERTOOK PRAGUE, WHICH HAD BECOME OLD AND DECADENT.

BY THEN ITS AILING MAGICIANS DID LITTLE BUT BICKER AMONG THE SLUMS OF THE OLD GHETTO.

ARE YOU LISTENING, LAD?

DO YOU KNOW WHAT THE IMPORTANT FACTS ARE HERE?

OH YES, SIR.

JUNIOR MINISTER FOR TRADE EYES CZECH DEAL

"I know what's important."

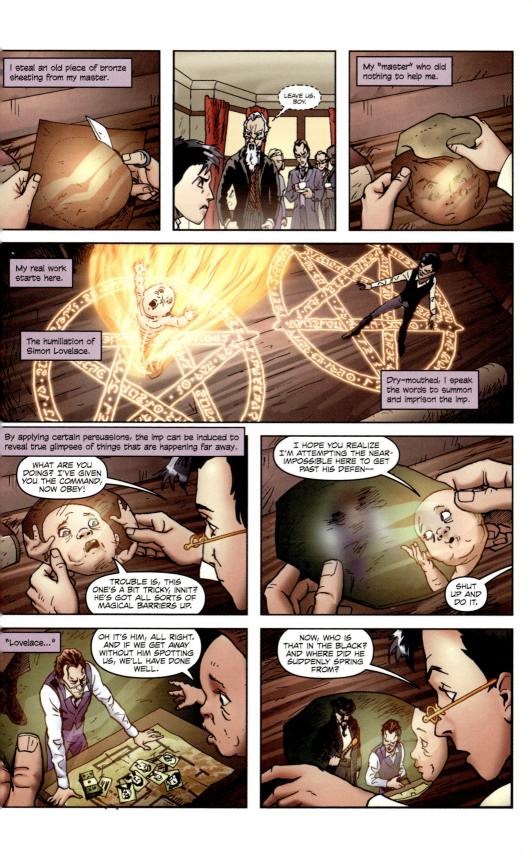

NOW.

I KNEW IT WAS GOING TO BE A DECENT SCRAP, AND I FIGURED WHAT WOULD ANNOY HIM MOST WAS TO APPEAR AS ANOTHER BOY OF ABOUT THE SAME AGE.

HE CAME OUT FIGHTING THOUGH, I'LL GIVE HIM THAT.

I CHARGE YOU TO--

NATHANIEL, EH? VERY POSH. DOESN'T REALLY SUIT YOU.

THAT'S NOT MY TRUE NAME.

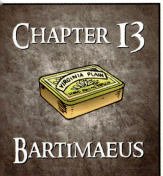

CHAPTER 13

BARTIMAEUS

AS I HOPED, HE FORGOT HIMSELF AND WENT FOR THE OBVIOUS ATTACK.

NATHANIEL.

AND USING HIS BIRTH NAME I SENT IT STRAIGHT BACK AT HIM.

ZZZZKKKKKKKKK

CAREFUL. NEARLY TOOK YOUR OWN HEAD OFF.

I KNOW A WAY YOU'LL STILL OBEY ME.

THE MOMENT YOU'VE GONE ON YOUR NEXT TASK, I SHALL CAST A SPELL OF INDEFINITE CONFINEMENT, BINDING YOU INTO THIS TIN.

UNFORTUNATELY FOR ME, HE WAS AN UNUSUALLY CLEVER AND RESOURCEFUL CHILD.

I have broken the cardinal rule.

The demon knows my birth name.

Panic wells up in my throat.

The cardinal rule... if you break that, you give yourself up for lost. Demons always find a way.

CHAPTER 14

NATHANIEL

No. I have only to work the confinement spell and everything will be fine.

I clasp my hands together to stop them shaking.

"Demons are very, very wicked. They will hurt you if they can."

"I'm worried about the boy. He barely touched his sandwich."

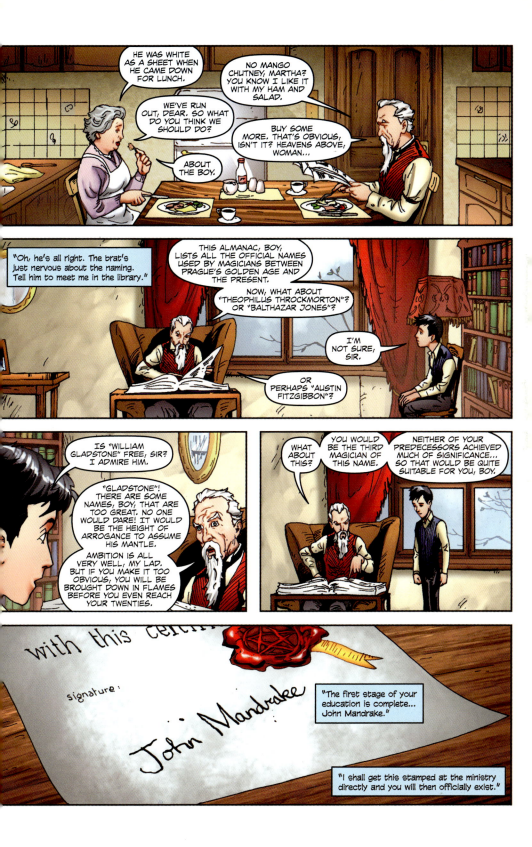

I sit on the backseat, as far away from the other passengers as possible.

Magicians are not known for catching public transport.

It is easy to see that the other passengers have no power.

Their conversations seem to be about nothing.

PLOPPP

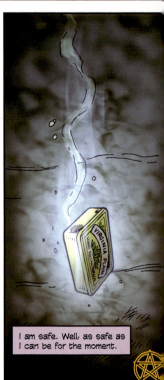

I am safe. Well, as safe as I can be for the moment.

WHEN I FLEW OUT OF THE BOY'S ATTIC WINDOW, MY HEAD WAS SO FULL OF PLANS AND STRATAGEMS THAT I FLEW STRAIGHT INTO A CHIMNEY. THAT'S WHAT FAKE FREEDOM DOES FOR YOU.

OFF I WENT, ONE OF A MILLION PIGEONS IN THE GREAT METROPOLIS. BUT MY FREEDOM WAS AN ILLUSION.

MY YOUNG MASTER HAD MADE IT QUITE CLEAR WHAT WOULD HAPPEN IF I FAILED TO CARRY OUT MY MISSION TO SPY ON SIMON LOVELACE.

CHAPTER 15

BARTIMAEUS

THE BOY HAD TOLD ME HOW HE HAD OBSERVED THE AMULET BEING DELIVERED TO LOVELACE BY A SWARTHY, BLACK-BEARDED STRANGER IN THE DEAD OF NIGHT.

THE AMULET HAD EVIDENTLY BEEN STOLEN. ALL THE BOY WANTED WAS FOR ME TO FIND OUT THE DETAILS SO HE COULD EXPOSE AND HUMILIATE LOVELACE.

THAT WAS ALL.

I STARTED BY HEADING BACK TO WATCH LOVELACE'S PLACE. I WAS BOUND TO HAVE TO WAIT FOR AN HOUR OR SO.

THREE DAYS I WAITED.

THREE WHOLE DAYS.

EVERY EVENING, SEARCH SPHERES LEFT TO HUNT FOR THE AMULET. EVERY DAWN THEY RETURNED.

MORE OMINOUSLY, UNSPEAKABLE THINGS PROWLED AROUND THE GROUNDS INSIDE.

MY ONLY COMPANY WAS A LOVESICK PIGEON.

IT WAS TEMPTING TO TURN INTO AN ALLEY CAT. BUT THAT WOULD BE TOO RISKY.

ON THE MORNING OF THE THIRD DAY, SOMETHING HAPPENED AT LAST.

A MESSENGER IMP LEFT LOVELACE'S COMPOUND.

PINN'S ACCOUTREMENTS— WHAT'S THAT?

THAT IS EASY TO ANSWER, O HE WHO IS TERRIBLE AND GREAT. IT IS THE MOST PRESTIGIOUS SUPPLIER OF MAGICAL ARTIFACTS IN LONDON.

SO IF A MAGICIAN WANTED TO BUY AN ARTIFACT, HE WOULD GO TO PINN'S?

YES.

YES WHAT?

I'M SORRY, O MAJESTIC ONE, IT'S DIFFICULT TO THINK OF NEW TITLES WHEN YOUR QUESTIONS ARE SO SHORT.

ONE MORE QUESTION. WHAT SERVANTS DOES LOVELACE EMPLOY?

I DO NOT HAVE ACCESS TO THE MAGICIAN'S INNER CHAMBERS, O MIRACULOUS ONE.

IF THAT IS ALL, O ACE ONE, MIGHT IT BE POSSIBLE TO MOVE THIS VERY HEAVY ROCK?

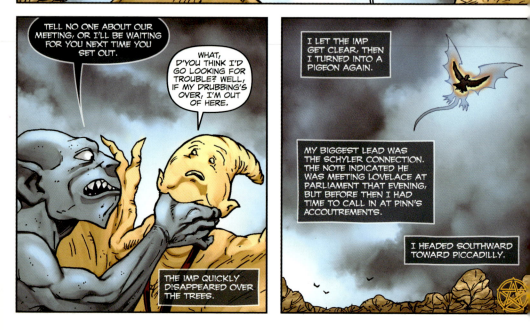

TELL NO ONE ABOUT OUR MEETING, OR I'LL BE WAITING FOR YOU NEXT TIME YOU SET OUT.

WHAT, D'YOU THINK I'D GO LOOKING FOR TROUBLE? WELL, IF MY DRUBBING'S OVER, I'M OUT OF HERE.

THE IMP QUICKLY DISAPPEARED OVER THE TREES.

I LET THE IMP GET CLEAR, THEN I TURNED INTO A PIGEON AGAIN.

MY BIGGEST LEAD WAS THE SCHYLER CONNECTION. THE NOTE INDICATED HE WAS MEETING LOVELACE AT PARLIAMENT THAT EVENING, BUT BEFORE THEN I HAD TIME TO CALL IN AT PINN'S ACCOUTREMENTS.

I HEADED SOUTHWARD TOWARD PICCADILLY.

PINN'S ACCOUTREMENTS LOOKED LIKE A PALACE THAT HAD BEEN DROPPED ONTO THE STREET BY A GANG OF KNACKERED DJINN.

Pinn's ACCOUTREMENTS

I GOT THERE JUST IN TIME TO SEE AN IMMENSELY FAT MAN PUT A "CLOSED" SIGN ON THE DOOR AND HAIL A CAB.

I TOOK THIS TO BE SHOLTO PINN HIMSELF.

CHAPTER 16

BARTIMAEUS

I KNOCKED ANYWAY. LOUDLY. THE BOY WHO ANSWERED...

MESSAGE HERE FOR MR. SHOLTO FROM SIMON LOVELACE.

HE'S OUT. COME BACK LATER.

...WAS REALLY A FOLIOT ON THE SECOND PLANE.

DON'T WORRY, I'LL WAIT.

I'M NOT SUPPOSED TO LET ANYONE IN...HEY.

WOW. NOT MANY PEOPLE GET TO WORK IN A PLACE THIS POSH.

YOU'RE CERTAINLY RIGHT THERE.

STILL, I BET YOU PROBABLY GET STUCK WITH ALL THE HEAVY LIFTING AND CLEANING, EH?

YOU CHEEKY FUNGUS! THE MASTER VALUES ME MORE THAN THAT. I AM HIS ASSISTANT!

I KNEW THEN THAT I WAS DEALING WITH A COLLABORATOR OF THE WORST KIND.

I ENGAGED HIM WITH SICKENING FLATTERY FOR SEVERAL MINUTES BEFORE GETTING DOWN TO BUSINESS.

YOU HAD ANYTHING FAMOUS IN HERE, THEN?

THE HIGHLIGHT OF LAST YEAR WAS NEFERTITI'S ANKLE BRACELET. THAT WAS A SENSATION!

ALL A BIT OVER MY HEAD, GUV'NOR. I'LL TELL YOU SOMETHING I'VE HEARD OF... THAT AMULET OF SAMARAD THING?

YOU MEAN THE AMULET OF SAMARKAND, AND THERE YOU SHOW YOUR IGNORANCE.

"The Amulet was the property of the British Government until it was stolen six months ago. We would never handle stolen property."

"And there was a murder, too. Grisly and horrible. Not one alarm or magical trap was triggered. But there was poor old Mr. Beecham lying beside its empty case in a pool of blood...and the Amulet was gone."

THAT'S TERRIBLE, GUV'NOR, A MOST TERRIBLE THING.

I LOOKED AS MOURNFUL AS AN IMP COULD, BUT INSIDE I WAS CROWING WITH TRIUMPH.

SO LOVELACE HADN'T ONLY NICKED THE AMULET, HE'D HAD MURDER COMMITTED TO GET IT.

AND ON TOP OF THAT, HE'D STOLEN IT FROM HIS OWN GOVERNMENT... AND THAT WAS TREASON.

WELL, IF THIS DIDN'T PLEASE THE KID THEN I WAS A MONKFISH.

THAT AMULET MUST BE QUITE SOMETHING. USEFUL PIECE, IS IT?

IT IS SAID TO CONTAIN A MOST POWERFUL BEING.

"Something from the deepest areas of the Other Place, where chaos rules.

"The Amulet is claimed to protect the wearer against any attack by--"

THE FOLIOT BROKE OFF WITH A SUDDEN GASP...

-GULP-

YOU'VE HURT THE MASTER. ANYWAY, IT'S TOO LATE FOR YOU. I'VE SOUNDED THE ALARM. THE AUTHORITIES HAVE SENT AN AF--

YEAH, YEAH.

I CHANGED INTO A FALCON. HE WASN'T EXPECTING THAT, BUT WHAT DID HE KNOW?

I SHOT OVER HIS HEAD, LEAVING A LITTLE FAREWELL DROPPING TO REMEMBER ME BY.

I BURST OUT AT LAST INTO THE FREEDOM OF THE AIR.

UPON WHICH, A NET OF SILVER THREADS DRAGGED ME DOWN TO THE COLD PAVEMENT.

THE THREADS HUNG TO ME WITH THE AGONIZING TOUCH OF SILVER.

I COULD NOT CHANGE.

I COULD NOT WORK ANY MAGIC, GREAT OR SMALL.

SOMEWHERE, I HEARD SIMPKIN LAUGHING, LONG AND SHRILL.

MY MIND WAS POISONED. DARKNESS SWATHED THE FALCON AND, AS IF IT WERE A GUTTERING CANDLE, SNUFFED ITS INTELLIGENCE OUT.

Silent onlookers stand on the sidewalks watching the procession of cars. Their faces are sullen, even hostile.

Most of them look thin and drawn and cold.

I have a name. I am on my way to Parliament.

A Government vigilance sphere hangs in the air and relays the scene to hidden eyes. We join the queue of the great and the good to go inside.

I have arrived.

I CAN'T WAIT TO SEE IF CAFTANS ARE STILL IN THIS YEAR.

MARTHA, PLEASE.

TIME THEN FOR YOUR FINAL WARNING. TONIGHT, YOU WILL BE REPRESENTING ME. PUT A FOOT OUT OF LINE AND YOU'LL RUIN MY REPUTATION.

IF YOU EMBARRASS ME IN ANY WAY, BOY, THEN I SHALL TAKE A LEAF FROM DISRAELI'S BOOK AND TURN YOU INTO A SOLID IRON STATUE.

DO YOU UNDERSTAND?

YES, SIR.

I have arrived.

CHAPTER 18

NATHANIEL

I DO LOVE TO WATCH THE FAMOUS ONES... SUCH A PLEASURE.

"That's Mr. Duvall, the Chief of Police. I met him once, John—what a charming man."

SHOULDN'T WE... YOU KNOW...TALK TO SOMEONE?

I THOUGHT I TOLD YOU TO KEEP QUIET, BOY.

"That's Maurice Schyler. He's something in the Government. I don't know what."

OH, AND THAT'S QUENTIN MAKEPEACE, THE PRIME MINISTER'S FAVORITE PLAYWRIGHT.

"Don't tell Mr. Underwood, but I think he's rather marvelous. His plays are so romantic."

"Jessica Whitwell, she's something to do with Security. Caught those Czech infiltrators ten years ago."

"Good heavens!"

"That's the merchant, Sholto Pinn.

"Whatever happened to him? Poor soul."

I feel suddenly reduced to insignificance. The unrated apprentice of an unrated magician.

AND OF COURSE YOU KNOW ...FROM THAT RATHER UNFORTUNATE INCIDENT LAST YEAR.

"That's the Junior Minister for Trade—Simon Lovelace."

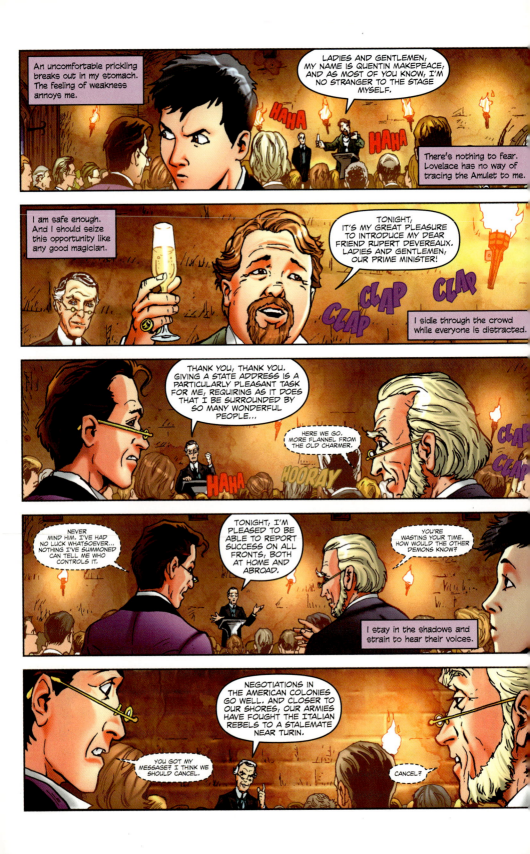

CHAPTER 19

NATHANIEL

The sphere shatters and the elementals trapped inside recoil from each other with ferocious and savage force.

Air, earth, fire, and water.

People are blown backwards.

Pelted with rocks.

Lacerated with fire.

And deluged with water.

The crowd are sent sprawling like skittles.

Night Police swarm over the river terrace.

The Prime Minister has already gone, whisked away to safety by a powerful afrit.

Most of the crowd weren't so lucky.

I find Mrs. Underwood and feel a little teary with relief.

ARE YOU ALL RIGHT?

YES. I THINK SO. BUT WHERE'S ARTHUR?

I spot him looking rather dazed.

ANYONE SEE WHAT HAPPENED?

ALL I CAN HOPE IS THAT WHAT HAPPENED TONIGHT WILL ENCOURAGE THEM TO GIVE ME MORE FUNDS.

IF THEY DON'T, WHAT CAN THEY EXPECT? WITH A MEASLY DEPARTMENT OF SIX MAGICIANS. I'M NOT A MIRACLE WORKER!

I DON'T THINK ANYONE IS BLAMING YOU FOR THE THEFTS, DEAR.

NO, BUT THEY WILL SOON.

WE'RE HOME.

MARK MY WORDS— AFTER TONIGHT, ANYONE CAUGHT IN POSSESSION OF STOLEN MAGICAL PROPERTY WILL SUFFER THE MOST SEVERE PENALTY.

THEY WON'T DIE EASILY, YOU CAN BE SURE OF THAT.

SLAM

HOT CHOCOLATE BEFORE BED, DEAR?

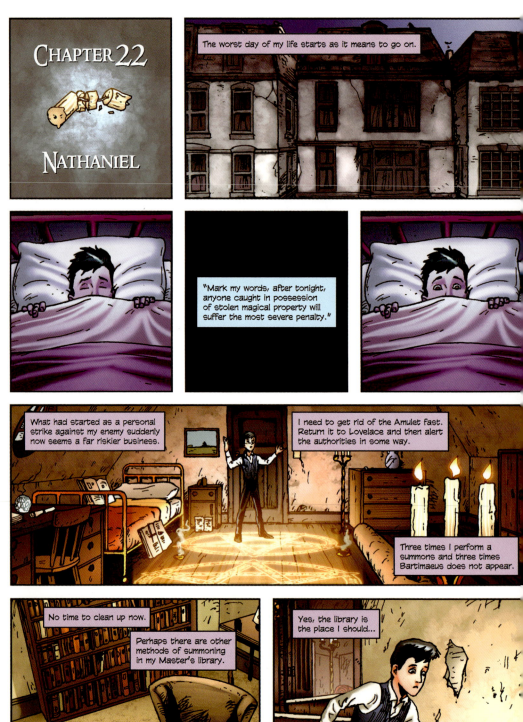

...begin.

YOU LITTLE RUFFIAN! YOU COULD HAVE KILLED ME!

WHACK!

I'M SORRY, SIR. YOU NEVER COME UP HERE...I DIDN'T EXPECT...

I WAS COMING TO TELL YOU OUR AFTERNOON PRACTICE SESSION WILL HAVE TO WAIT.

I'VE HAD A CALL TO GO INTO...

WHAT'S THAT SMELL?

PERHAPS I DIDN'T WASH WELL ENOUGH THIS MORNING, SIR.

IT'S NOT YOUR SCENT, BOY, UNPLEASANT THOUGH THAT IS.

ROSEMARY...LAUREL... YOU, BOY, HAVE THE GENERAL SMELL OF A SUMMONING ABOUT YOUR PERSON....I WISH TO SEE YOUR ROOM.

PLEASE DON'T, SIR. IT'S SUCH A MESS.

YOU... YOU...

YOU HAVE DISOBEYED ME IN A HUNDRED WAYS! YOU HAVE RISKED YOUR OWN LIFE AND THE LIVES OF EVERYONE IN THIS HOUSE. YOU HAVE DABBLED WITH MAGICS YOU CANNOT HOPE TO COMPREHEND.

I SHOULD HAVE KNOWN YOU WERE NOT TO BE TRUSTED LAST YEAR, WHEN YOUR WILLFUL ACT OF VIOLENCE AGAINST SIMON LOVELACE NEARLY RUINED MY CAREER.

IF I DIDN'T HAVE TO GO INTO THE MINISTRY URGENTLY, I WOULD DEAL WITH YOU RIGHT NOW.

YOU ARE CONFINED TO YOUR ROOM. REMAIN THERE AND REFLECT UPON THE RUIN OF YOUR CAREER AND PROBABLY YOUR LIFE. I WILL RETURN FOR YOU, BOY.

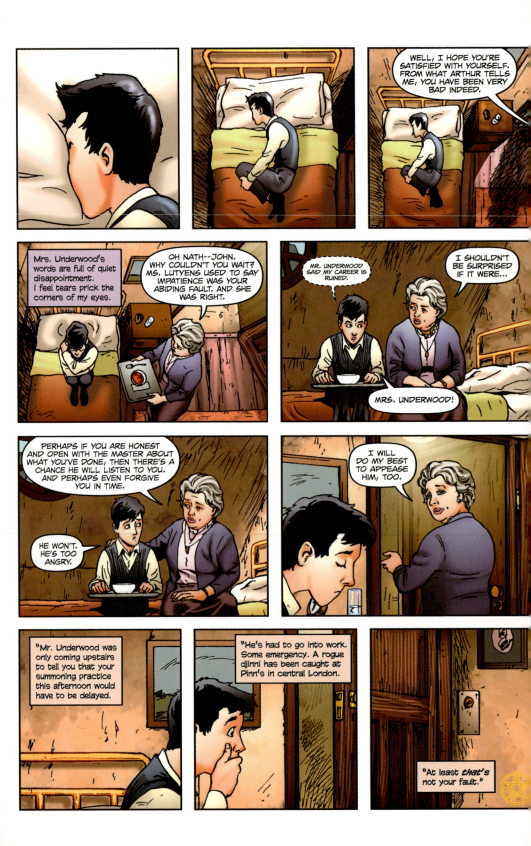

WELL, I HOPE YOU'RE SATISFIED WITH YOURSELF. FROM WHAT ARTHUR TELLS ME, YOU HAVE BEEN VERY BAD INDEED.

Mrs. Underwood's words are full of quiet disappointment. I feel tears prick the corners of my eyes.

OH NATH--JOHN. WHY COULDN'T YOU WAIT? MS. LUTYENS USED TO SAY IMPATIENCE WAS YOUR ABIDING FAULT. AND SHE WAS RIGHT.

MR. UNDERWOOD SAID MY CAREER IS RUINED.

I SHOULDN'T BE SURPRISED IF IT WERE...

MRS. UNDERWOOD!

PERHAPS IF YOU ARE HONEST AND OPEN WITH THE MASTER ABOUT WHAT YOU'VE DONE, THEN THERE'S A CHANCE HE WILL LISTEN TO YOU. AND PERHAPS EVEN FORGIVE YOU IN TIME.

HE WON'T. HE'S TOO ANGRY.

I WILL DO MY BEST TO APPEASE HIM, TOO.

"Mr. Underwood was only coming upstairs to tell you that your summoning practice this afternoon would have to be delayed.

"He's had to go into work. Some emergency. A rogue djinni has been caught at Pinn's in central London.

"At least *that's* not your fault."

AN ENORMOUS BLACK RAVEN SWOOPED DOWN, FOLLOWED BY ANOTHER ONE.

THERE WAS A BLUR OF MOVEMENT, A SNAP, AND TWO GULPS.

THEN THE TWO UTUKKU WERE GONE.

EVEN I DON'T SEE *THAT* EVERY DAY.

ONE OF THE RAVENS GAVE A SHIMMY AND TOOK ON AN ALL-TOO-FAMILIAR GUISE...

OH. HELLO.

HELLO, BARTIMAEUS.

Chapter 24

Bartimaeus

AND JABOR, TOO. HOW NICE OF YOU BOTH TO COME.

WE THOUGHT YOU MIGHT BE LONELY, BARTIMAEUS.

NOW, TELL US WHERE YOU SECRETED THE AMULET OF SAMARKAND AND IF YOU SPEAK RAPIDLY, WE MIGHT HAVE TIME TO DESTROY THE ORB BEFORE YOU PERISH.

REVERSE THAT SEQUENCE AND YOU COULD HAVE YOURSELVES A DEAL.

WE BOTH KNOW THAT IF I TELL YOU THE LOCATION, YOU'LL LEAVE ME TO DIE. THEREFORE, I'LL OBVIOUSLY GIVE YOU FALSE INFORMATION JUST TO SPITE YOU. SO ANYTHING I SAY FROM IN HERE WILL BE WORTHLESS. AND THAT MEANS YOU'VE GOT TO LET ME OUT.

ANNOYING, BUT I SEE YOUR POINT.

THE KINDLY MAGICIANS WHO PUT ME IN HERE MENTIONED LEGIONS OF HORLAS AND UTUKKU—I SHOULD THINK THAT'S THEM ARRIVING NOW... I DOUBT EVEN JABOR CAN SWALLOW THEM ALL.

SO PERHAPS WE COULD CONTINUE THIS DISCUSSION A LITTLE LATER?

AGREED.

PALE-FACED HORLAS FOUGHT TO GET OUT OF THE PORTAL, HOLDING THEIR LITTLE TRIDENTS AND SILVER NETS IN THEIR STICK-THIN ARMS.

IT WAS TIME TO GO.

CCCKKKKKKKKKKKKKKKKKKKKK!

FROM A POCKET IN HIS COAT, FAQUARL PRODUCED A RING OF IRON SOLDERED TO A METAL ROD. (WELL, HE WOULDN'T WANT TO TOUCH THE IRON—UGH!)

FIIIZZZZZZZZZZZZZ

MARVELOUS. IF ONLY WE'D HAD A DRUM ROLL.

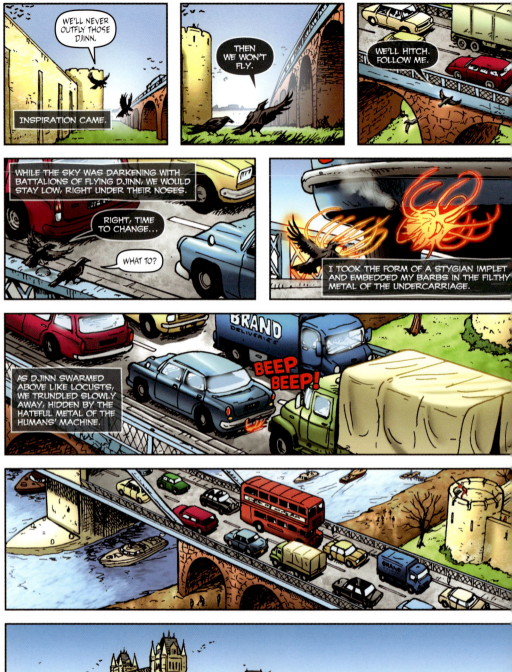

HERE'S MY FINAL OFFER. GUIDE ME TO THE AMULET AND I PROMISE THAT, WHATEVER YOU SUFFER, LOVELACE WILL TAKE YOU ON AFTERWARDS AND...

FOR A COUPLE OF SECONDS, NO ONE MOVED.

YOU SMELL OF PETROL.

FAQUARL BEGAN A GESTURE. I SENSED HIS REGRETFUL INTENTION.

WHY DID I ACT THEN? PURE SELF-INTEREST. BECAUSE WITH FAQUARL MOMENTARILY DISTRACTED, IT WAS THE PERFECT OPPORTUNITY TO ESCAPE.

AND IF I HAPPENED TO SAVE THE GIRL TOO... WELL, IT WAS ONLY FAIR. IT WAS SHE WHO GAVE ME THE IDEA, AFTER ALL

DON'T YOU...

WWHHHHOOOSH!

EEEEEEEEEEEEEKKK!

IN A MOMENT, I WAS IN THE AIR AND HURTLING AT TOP SPEED TOWARD MY STUPID, MISBEGOTTEN MASTER.

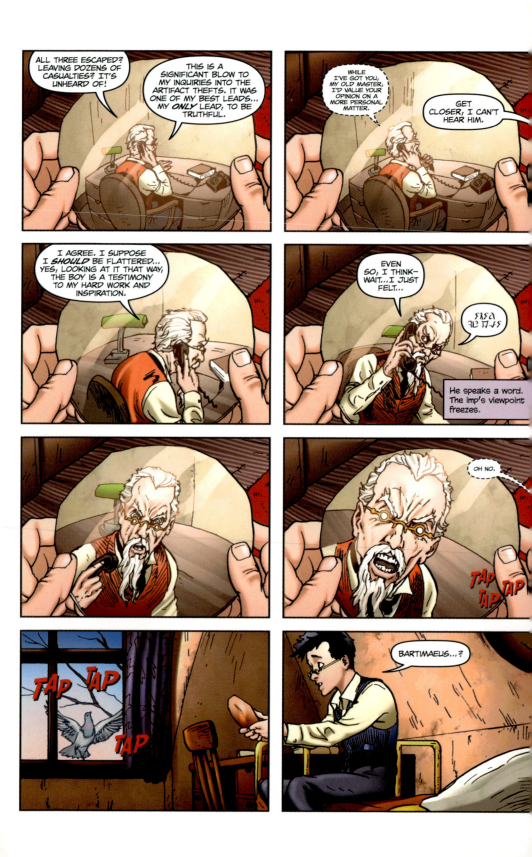

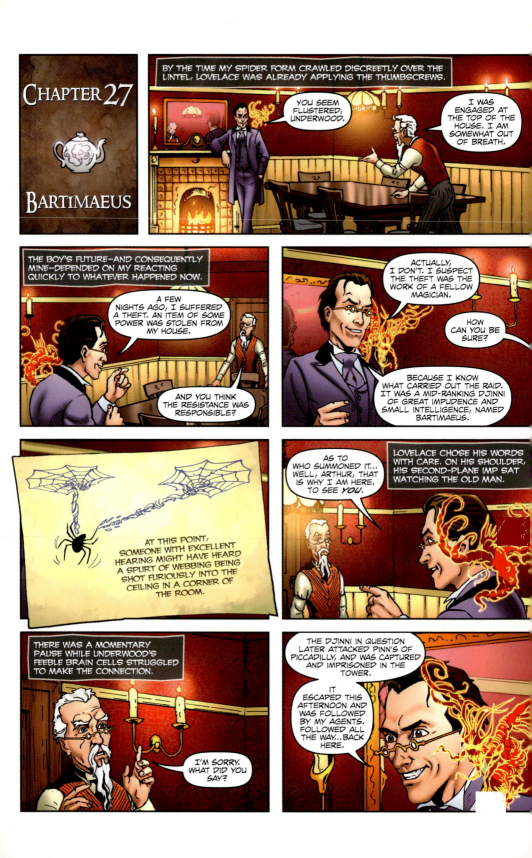

CHAPTER 27

BARTIMAEUS

BY THE TIME MY SPIDER FORM CRAWLED DISCREETLY OVER THE LINTEL, LOVELACE WAS ALREADY APPLYING THE THUMBSCREWS.

YOU SEEM FLUSTERED, UNDERWOOD.

I WAS ENGAGED AT THE TOP OF THE HOUSE. I AM SOMEWHAT OUT OF BREATH.

THE BOY'S FUTURE—AND CONSEQUENTLY MINE—DEPENDED ON MY REACTING QUICKLY TO WHATEVER HAPPENED NOW.

A FEW NIGHTS AGO, I SUFFERED A THEFT. AN ITEM OF SOME POWER WAS STOLEN FROM MY HOUSE.

AND YOU THINK THE RESISTANCE WAS RESPONSIBLE?

ACTUALLY, I DON'T. I SUSPECT THE THEFT WAS THE WORK OF A FELLOW MAGICIAN.

HOW CAN YOU BE SURE?

BECAUSE I KNOW WHAT CARRIED OUT THE RAID. IT WAS A MID-RANKING DJINNI OF GREAT IMPUDENCE AND SMALL INTELLIGENCE, NAMED BARTIMAEUS.

AT THIS POINT, SOMEONE WITH EXCELLENT HEARING MIGHT HAVE HEARD A SPURT OF WEBBING BEING SHOT FURIOUSLY INTO THE CEILING IN A CORNER OF THE ROOM.

AS TO WHO SUMMONED IT... WELL, ARTHUR, THAT IS WHY I AM HERE. TO SEE *YOU*.

LOVELACE CHOSE HIS WORDS WITH CARE. ON HIS SHOULDER, HIS SECOND-PLANE IMP SAT WATCHING THE OLD MAN.

THERE WAS A MOMENTARY PAUSE WHILE UNDERWOOD'S FEEBLE BRAIN CELLS STRUGGLED TO MAKE THE CONNECTION.

I'M SORRY. WHAT DID YOU SAY?

THE DJINNI IN QUESTION LATER ATTACKED PINN'S OF PICCADILLY, AND WAS CAPTURED AND IMPRISONED IN THE TOWER.

IT ESCAPED THIS AFTERNOON AND WAS FOLLOWED BY MY AGENTS. FOLLOWED ALL THE WAY...BACK HERE.

LOVELACE CLICKED HIS FINGERS AND HIS IMP SPRANG ONTO THE DINING ROOM TABLE. A BULB SWELLED AT THE END OF ITS FOUL TAIL AND...

KNOCK KNOCK

CHAPTER 28

NATHANIEL

Panic rushes through my head.

Slowly, steadily, over the last few days, everything has spiraled out of my control.

I hear Mrs. Underwood gently humming as she hurries around downstairs.

Mrs. Underwood... who I have placed in terrible danger.

Running and hiding are the advice of a treacherous demon. Not the actions of an honorable magician.

I know what I must do.

I arrive just in time to witness the moment of discovery.

HA! WELL, WELL, WHAT HAVE WE HERE?

NO... IT'S A TRICK... YOU'RE FRAMING ME. I DON'T KNOW HOW THAT GOT THERE...

HE'S TELLING THE TRUTH. I TOOK IT.

THE PERSON THAT YOU WANT IS ME.

WHAT ARE YOU GIBBERING ABOUT, YOU FOOL? GET OUT!

A MOMENT, ARTHUR. PERHAPS YOU'RE BEING TOO HASTY.

DON'T BE ABSURD! THIS STRIPLING CANNOT HAVE COMMITTED THE CRIME. HE WOULD HAVE NEEDED TO BYPASS BOTH OUR DEFENSES...

"Not to mention being able to summon a most powerful and sophisticated djinni.

"Oh."

BUT WHY WOULD YOU STEAL ANYTHING FROM ME?

I do not think my master has recognized what the Amulet really is. And that may yet save him.

IT WAS JUST A TRICK, SIR. A JOKE. I WANTED TO GET BACK AT YOU FOR HITTING ME THE TIME I RELEASED THE MITES.

THIS IS THE LAST STRAW, BOY! I WILL HAVE YOU UP BEFORE THE COURTS FOR THIS.

WE HAVE BOTH BEEN INCONVENIENCED, LOVELACE. HE HAS BETRAYED ME, AND FROM YOU HE HAS STOLEN THIS VALUABLE AMULET...

My master fell silent.

In that sudden, fatal instant, he realized what the Amulet was.

AND...AND WE SHALL BOTH SEE HIM SUITABLY PUNISHED, YES WE WILL. AND HE'LL REGRET THE DAY HE STOLE THE...ERR...THING.

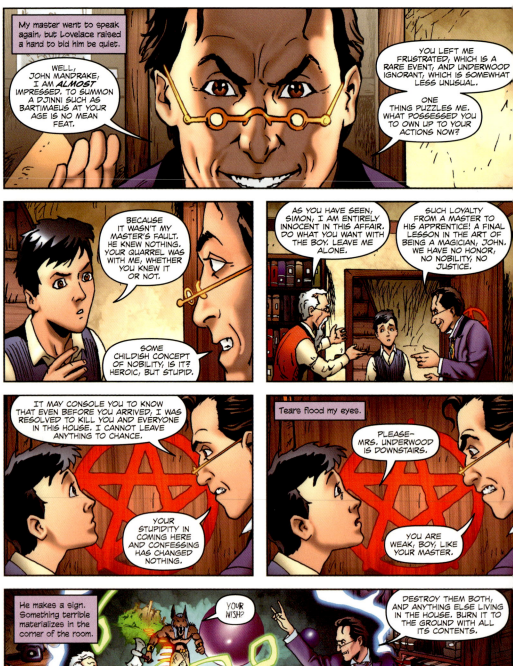

CHAPTER 29

BARTIMAEUS

I GIVE UNDERWOOD'S DESK THE CREDIT.

IT WAS AN OLD-FASHIONED, STURDY AFFAIR.

CRRRRRACCCCKKKK!

IN THE SECONDS IT TOOK JABOR TO SMASH IT, I BECAME A GARGOYLE, GRABBED MY YOUNG MASTER, AND RAN.

WE WENT ALMOST UNNOTICED.

UNDERWOOD SENT A BOLT OF BLUE FIRE CRACKING TOWARD LOVELACE...

BUT THE AMULET OF SAMARKAND ABSORBED THE ENTIRE ATTACK.

WE'D JUST GOT PAST THE MAIN LANDING...

WHEN WE HEARD UNDERWOOD'S SCREAM.

A MOMENT LATER...

A COLOSSAL EXPLOSION RIPPED THROUGH THE HOUSE.

AN OVERZEALOUS ATTACK, AND QUITE TYPICAL OF JABOR.

MRS. UNDERWOOD?

MRS. UNDERWOOD?!

I GOT BACK ON MY FEET, GRABBED THE BOY AGAIN, AND RAN.

THIS IS ALL MY FAULT!

YEP. BUT YOU CAN'T HELP HER NOW AND SHE WOULDN'T WANT YOU TO DIE, TOO. LIFE'S FOR THE LIVING AND... ERM...OH, FORGET IT.

PSYCHOLOGY OF THIS SORT IS NOT MY STRONG SUIT.

MY SCRYING GLASS!

COME ON! OUT!

I ASK YOU! JACKAL-HEADED DEATH ON HIS HEELS AND HE WAS DAWDLING FOR *THAT?*

ONE GOOD THING ABOUT JABOR...

WE NEED TO GET ONTO THE ROOF!

...HE TOOK HIS TIME.

I THINK THE BOY WAS IN SHOCK. IT SEEMED UNLIKELY, BUT MAYBE NOBODY HAD TRIED TO KILL HIM BEFORE.

THE ROOF SHIFTED WITH THE HEAT FROM BELOW.

IF WE JUST RAN, JABOR WOULD NAIL US WITH A DETONATION BEFORE WE'D GONE FIVE METERS.

NOW WAS VERY MUCH THE TIME TO THINK OF A BRILLIANT, WATERTIGHT PLAN.

FAILING THAT, I IMPROVISED.

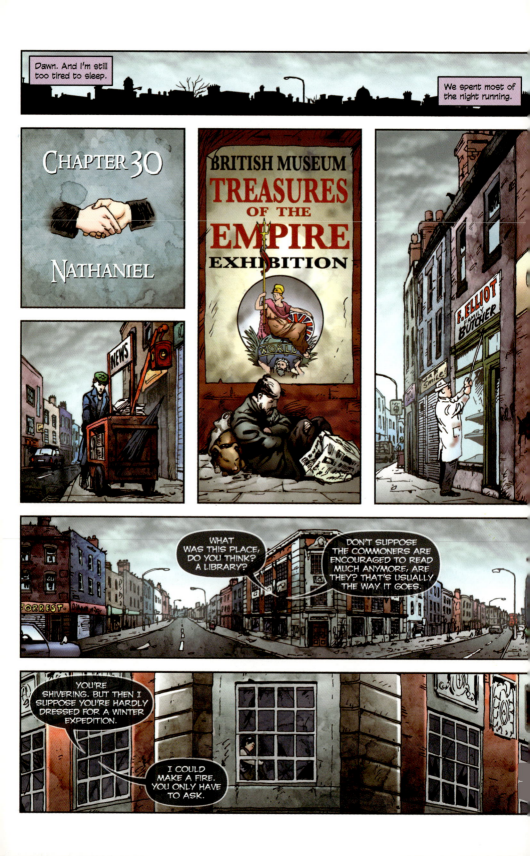

OR, OF COURSE, YOU COULD JUST READ THIS...

Conference of the Year

HEDDLEHAM HALL

DEVEREAUX

CATHCART

LOVELACE

"Bartimaeus, fly to Heddleham Hall now, get as close as you can, and find us a way to get in. Then return to me.

"I shall wait for you here. I need to sleep.

"Now go."

CHAPTER 32

NATHANIEL

HA HA HA HA

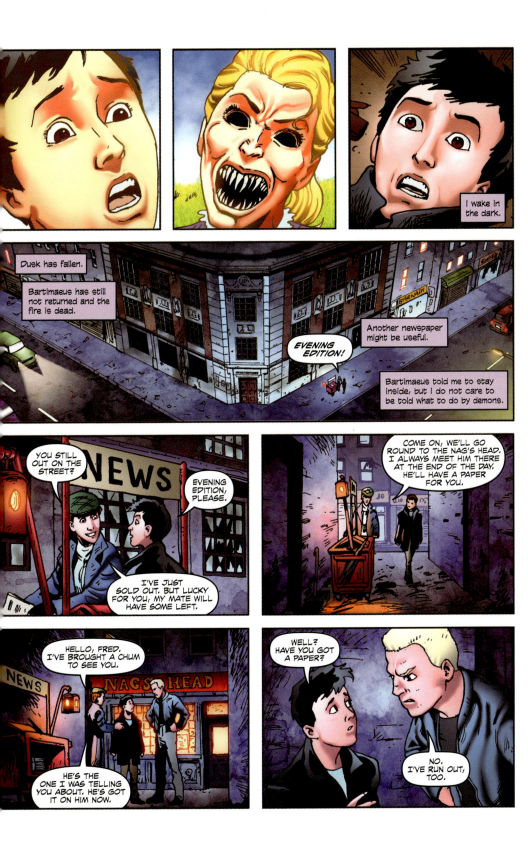

Fury overcomes dizziness and I set off in unsteady pursuit.

UHHHHHH

I strain to hear their words and edge nearer.

CLINK!

NHHACCCK!

SHALL I CUT HIS THROAT FOR YOU, KITTY?

NO... HE'S ONLY A STUPID KID. LET'S GO.

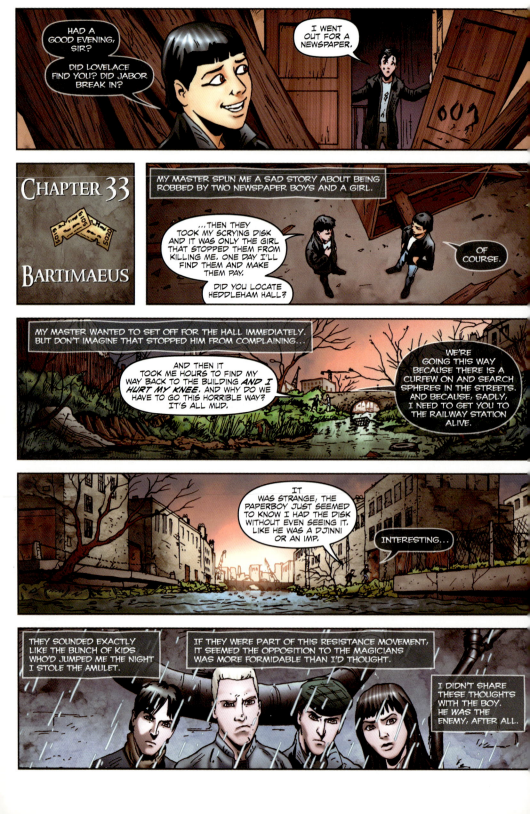

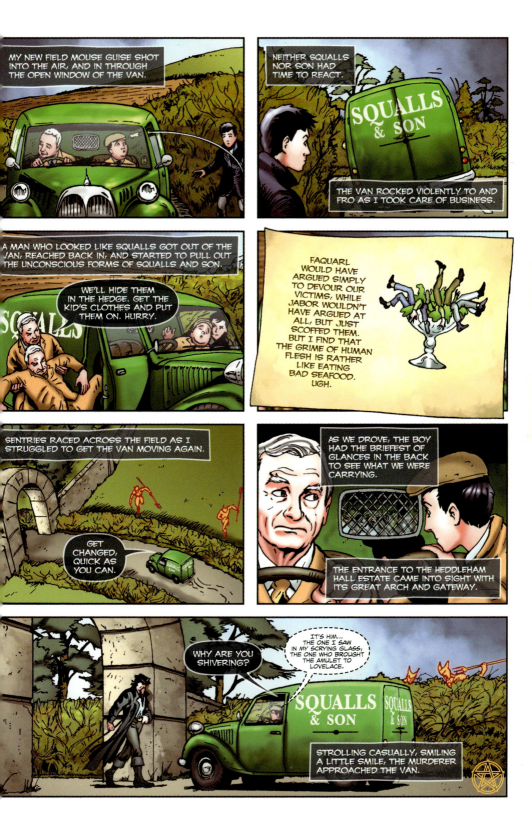

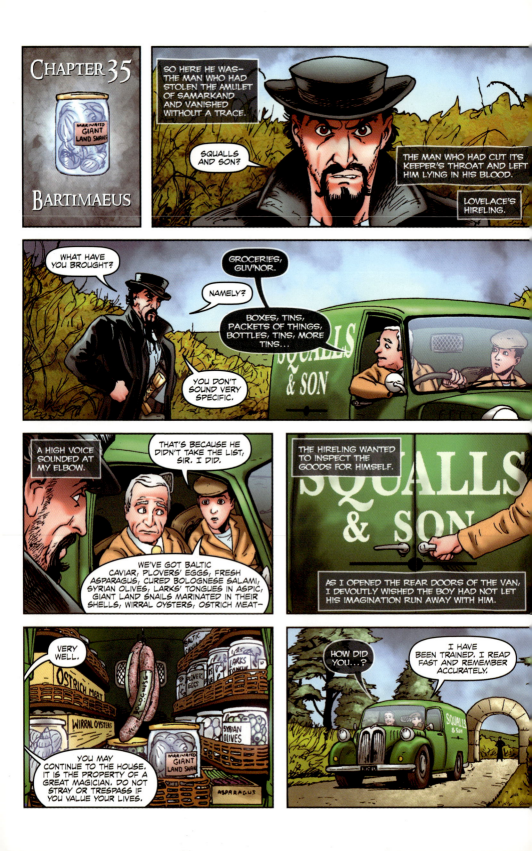

CHAPTER 35

MARINATED
GIANT
LAND SNAILS

BARTIMAEUS

SO HERE HE WAS—THE MAN WHO HAD STOLEN THE AMULET OF SAMARKAND AND VANISHED WITHOUT A TRACE.

SQUALLS AND SON?

THE MAN WHO HAD CUT ITS KEEPER'S THROAT AND LEFT HIM LYING IN HIS BLOOD.

LOVELACE'S HIRELING.

WHAT HAVE YOU BROUGHT?

GROCERIES, GUV'NOR.

NAMELY?

BOXES, TINS, PACKETS OF THINGS, BOTTLES, TINS, MORE TINS...

YOU DON'T SOUND VERY SPECIFIC.

SQUALLS & SON

A HIGH VOICE SOUNDED AT MY ELBOW.

THAT'S BECAUSE HE DIDN'T TAKE THE LIST, SIR. I DID.

WE'VE GOT BALTIC CAVIAR, PLOVERS' EGGS, FRESH ASPARAGUS, CURED BOLOGNESE SALAMI, SYRIAN OLIVES, LARKS' TONGUES IN ASPIC, GIANT LAND SNAILS MARINATED IN THEIR SHELLS, WIRRAL OYSTERS, OSTRICH MEAT—

THE HIRELING WANTED TO INSPECT THE GOODS FOR HIMSELF.

SQUALLS & SON

AS I OPENED THE REAR DOORS OF THE VAN, I DEVOUTLY WISHED THE BOY HAD NOT LET HIS IMAGINATION RUN AWAY WITH HIM.

VERY WELL.

OSTRICH MEAT
BALTIC CAVIAR
LARKS TONGUE
BOLOGNESE
PLOVERS EGGS
WIRRAL OYSTERS
SYRIAN OLIVES
MARINATED GIANT LAND SNAILS
ASPARAGUS

YOU MAY CONTINUE TO THE HOUSE. IT IS THE PROPERTY OF A GREAT MAGICIAN. DO NOT STRAY OR TRESPASS IF YOU VALUE YOUR LIVES.

HOW DID YOU...?

I HAVE BEEN TRAINED. I READ FAST AND REMEMBER ACCURATELY.

SQUALLS & SON

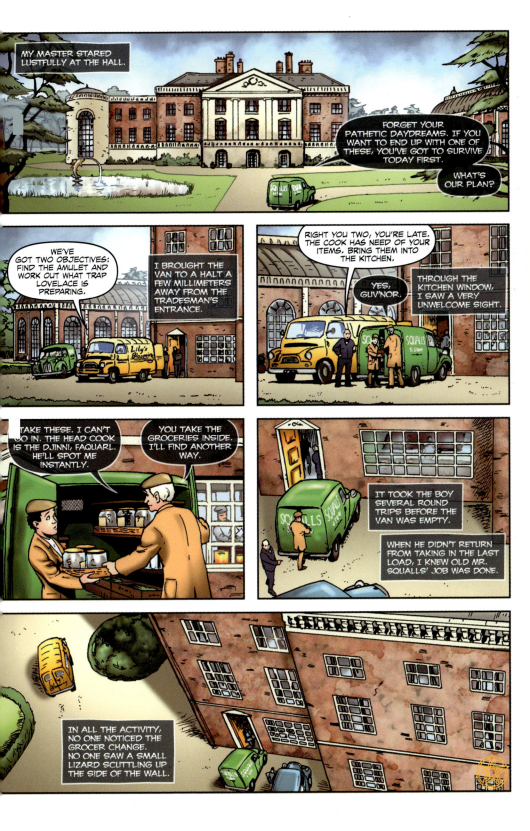

I could be caught at any moment, but I feel a strange exhilaration.

I'm taking control of events.

I'm the one doing the hunting.

CHAPTER 36

NATHANIEL

I follow a boy about my size to the cloakroom.

WHACK!

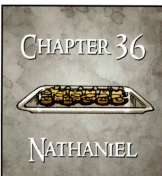

I leave him gagged and bound and hidden in a cubicle.

LIKE ANIMALS, AREN'T THEY? BLOODY MAGICIANS.

I watch Lovelace smiling at his guests. Mrs. Underwood died because he stole the Amulet. Now I will destroy him.

I SAW THE ROOM FOR THE FIRST TIME ONLY THIS MORNING. SIMON SAID IT WOULD TAKE MY BREATH AWAY AND HE WAS RIGHT.

THE CARPET HAS TO BE SEEN TO BE BELIEVED!

THANK GOODNESS-- FOOD! FAMISHING JOURNEY FROM LONDON.

ARE YOU SERVING THOSE, BOY, OR TAKING THEM FOR A WALK?

SORRY, SIR.

I pick up a new tray and loiter until there is a sudden stir in the crowd...

LADIES AND GENTLEMEN! OUR BELOVED PRIME MINISTER, RUPERT DEVEREAUX....

ON BEHALF OF LADY AMANDA AND MYSELF, SIR, MAY I WELCOME YOU TO HEDDLEHAM HALL.

CLAP!

CLAP!

THE SPEECHES WILL BEGIN SHORTLY IN THE GRAND SALON, WHICH LADY AMANDA HAS REFURBISHED ESPECIALLY FOR TODAY.

I'M LOOKING FORWARD TO IT, LOVELACE.

WOULD YOU EXCUSE ME, SIR? I MUST JUST COLLECT SOME PROPS FOR MY OPENING SPEECH. THEN WE'LL BE READY FOR THE BIG EVENT.

CHAPTER 37

NATHANIEL

Lovelace sneaks away... with me on his trail.

Now I am the one doing the hunting.

I am careful not to make the slightest noise.

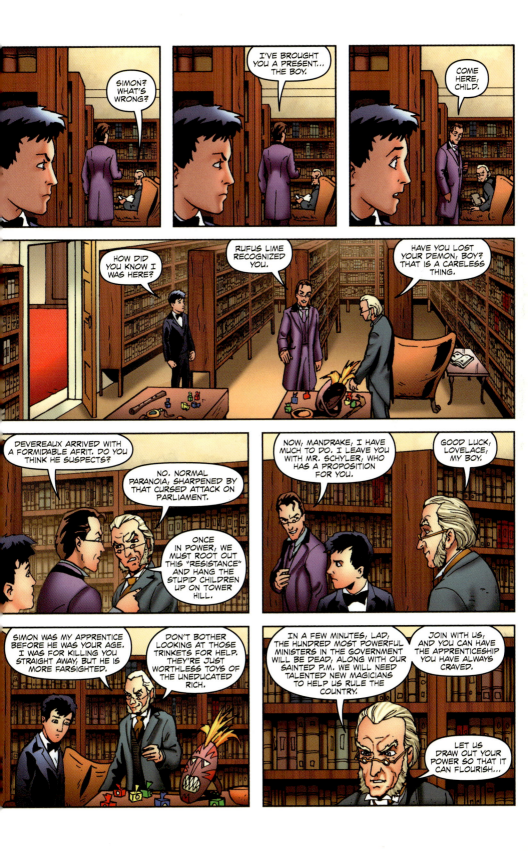

Six years of suppressed desire—to be recognized for what I am...to exercise power...to go to Parliament as a great minister of State...

Six years of suppressed desire...

DOES SIMON LOVELACE *REALLY* THINK I WILL JOIN HIM? AFTER EVERYTHING THAT HAS HAPPENED?

HE DOES....

THEN HE'S A FOOL. AN ARROGANT FOOL.

AFTER WHAT HE HAS DONE TO ME, HE COULD OFFER UP THE WORLD AND I'D REFUSE. JOIN HIM? I WOULD RATHER DIE.

VERY WELL.

ORDINARILY, I WOULD ENJOY KILLING YOU SLOWLY...BUT SADLY, TODAY I CANNOT SPARE THE TIME.

CHAPTER 38

BARTIMAEUS

I HOPED THE BOY COULD KEEP OUT OF TROUBLE LONG ENOUGH FOR ME TO REACH HIM.

GETTING IN WAS TAKING LONGER THAN I THOUGHT.

THE LIZARD SCUTTLED UP AND DOWN, BUT THE PLACE WAS TOO WELL-SEALED.

ONE WING OF THE HOUSE DREW MY ATTENTION. POWERFUL MAGICAL BARS CRISSCROSSED ALL THE WINDOWS AS FAR AS THE SEVENTH PLANE. BUT THEY WERE ON THE INSIDE...

MY CURIOSITY WAS PIQUED.

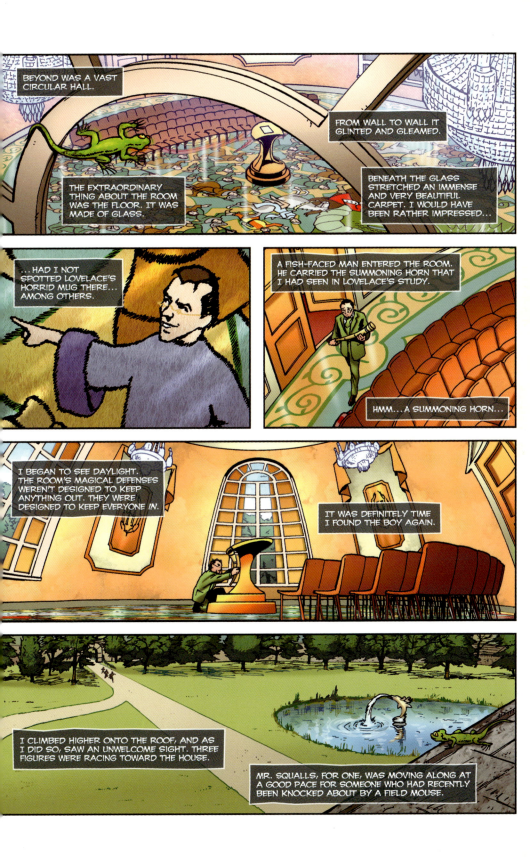

THE BEARDED MERCENARY SEEMED TO MOVE WITH SUPERHUMAN SPEED.

HIS STRIDES SEEMED ORDINARY ONES, BUT THEY ATE UP THE GROUND AT BLINDING PACE.

THEN I SAW HE WAS WEARING SEVEN-LEAGUE BOOTS. SO *THAT'S* HOW HE GOT AWAY WITH STEALING THE AMULET.

SEVEN-LEAGUE BOOTS = A POTENT MAGICAL DEVICE. EACH BOOT CONTAINS A CAPTIVE DJINNI WHO CAN BEND TIME AND SPACE.

I CHANGED FORM AGAIN.

THIS WASN'T THE TIME TO BE DISCREET.

MY FIRST DETONATION VAPORIZED A SMALL HONEYSUCKLE BY THE LAKE.

MY SECOND CAUGHT THE MERCENARY IN THE CHEST.

HE DISAPPEARED IN A MASS OF SAPPHIRE FLAMES.

ONLY TO REAPPEAR— VERY MUCH ALIVE.

I DELIVERED ANOTHER, MORE CONCENTRATED BLAST...

...TO NO EFFECT.

NOW *THAT* WAS ANNOYING.

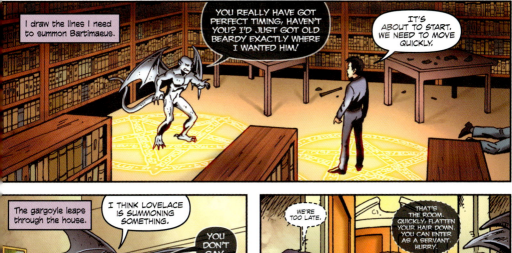

I draw the lines I need to summon Bartimaeus.

YOU REALLY HAVE GOT PERFECT TIMING, HAVEN'T YOU? I'D JUST GOT OLD BEARDY EXACTLY WHERE I WANTED HIM!

IT'S ABOUT TO START. WE NEED TO MOVE QUICKLY.

The gargoyle leaps through the house.

I THINK LOVELACE IS SUMMONING SOMETHING.

YOU DON'T SAY.

WE'RE TOO LATE.

THAT'S THE ROOM. QUICKLY, FLATTEN YOUR HAIR DOWN. YOU CAN ENTER AS A SERVANT. HURRY.

Bartimaeus changes into a new, much smaller form.

WHO ARE YOU?

THEY WANT SOMEONE EXTRA FOR THE DRINKS, SIR.

I can feel Bartimaeus as a small insect in my ear.

CLLICKKK

Behind us, the door swings shut. Locks click into position and huge bolts are drawn.

I'D LIKE TO WELCOME YOU ALL TO AN EXTRAORDINARY EVENT...

OH DEAR... NOW, THAT DOES SOUND OMINOUS.

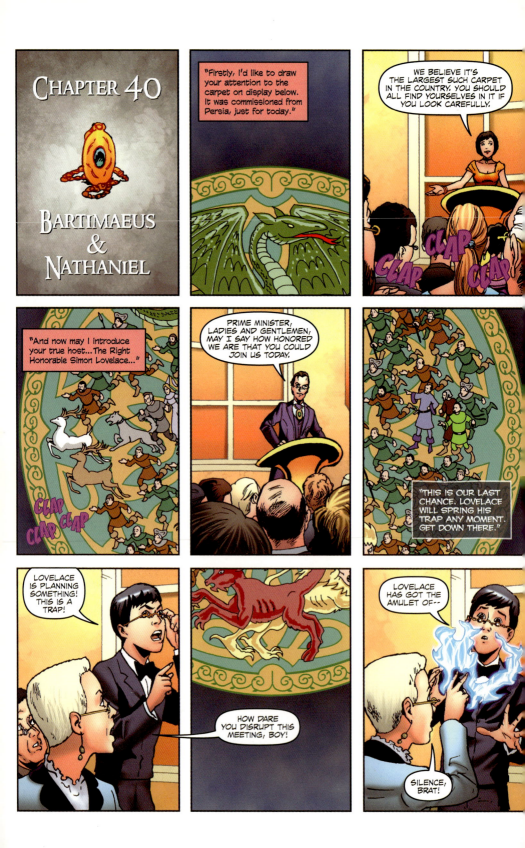

AFTER THAT, EVENTS HAPPENED FAST.

LOVELACE RAISED THE HORN TO HIS LIPS AND BLEW. IT MADE NO SOUND IN THE ROOM, BUT IN THE OTHER PLACE IT WOULD HAVE RUNG LOUD.

THE MAGICIANS UNDERSTOOD NOW. THEY LAUNCHED ATTACKS IN LOVELACE'S DIRECTION, BUT THE AMULET DID ITS WORK.

LOVELACE JUST SMOOTHED BACK HIS HAIR AND SMILED.

SOME MAGICIANS TRIED THE DOORS WITHOUT SUCCESS.

DEVEREAUX'S AFRIT ATTEMPTED TO FLY HIM OUT OF ONE OF THE WINDOWS; BUT THE MAGIC SEALS HELD FIRM. THEY BOTH TUMBLED BACK TO EARTH.

WHHWHAGG!!

I SAW A FLICKER IN THE AIR.

THEN SOMETHING TORE A HOLE IN THE REALITY OF THE WORLD AND STARTED TO PUSH ITS WAY THROUGH.

MY ESSENCE SHIVERED.

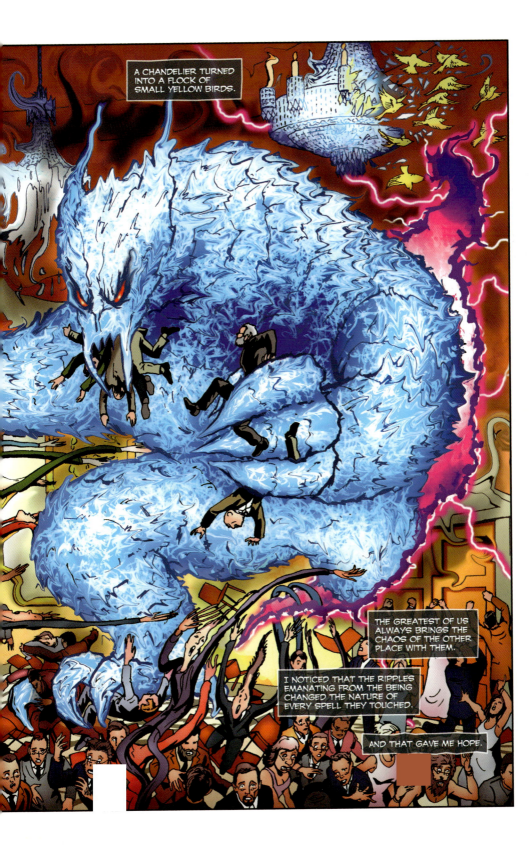

FIRST, THOUGH, I NEEDED TO GET RID OF JABOR.

I GOT INTO POSITION AND, WITH A CHEEKY SMILE, INVITED HIM TO CHARGE.

MY DEAR MASTER SCHYLER SUGGESTED THIS PLAN, AND AS ALWAYS HE WAS INSPIRED. HE WILL BE WATCHING US AT THIS VERY MOMENT.

I DOUBT IT. HE'S LYING DEAD UPSTAIRS.

HE FLEW AT ME IN RAGE.

I SIDESTEPPED HIM AND PUSHED HIM ON TOWARD THE RIFT.

DEAD?

HE WASN'T HAPPY.

HE'D GOTTEN TOO CLOSE AND THE RIFT HAD CAUGHT HIM. LIQUID STREAMS OF GREASY GRAY-BLACK STUFF SPIRALLED FROM HIS BODY. THAT WAS HIS ESSENCE GOING.

THAT'S RIGHT, I DIDN'T JUST ESCAPE. I KILLED HIM.

IF HE'D HAD HALF A BRAIN, HE COULD HAVE CHANGED INTO A GNAT OR SOMETHING WITH LESS BULK... BUT HE DIDN'T.

I HAD NO TIME FOR LONG GOOD-BYES. I HAD OTHER MATTERS TO ATTEND TO.

DON'T LIE TO ME, CHILD--

SIMON!

CHAPTER 42

BARTIMAEUS

TYPICAL OF THE KID, THAT WAS.

CHAPTER 43

BARTIMAEUS

SUNSET. THE DAY AFTER THE GREAT SUMMONING.

I PREFERRED YOUR OLD PLACE. THIS ONE SMELLS AND YOU HAVEN'T EVEN MOVED IN YET.

IT DOESN'T SMELL.

THE BOY HAD SPENT ALL DAY WITH MINISTERS AND POLICE, SPINNING AN OUTRAGEOUS YARN ABOUT HOW HE AND HIS POOR DEAD MASTER HAD FOUGHT AGAINST LOVELACE'S EVIL SCHEME.

IT DOES SMELL... OF FRESH PAINT AND PLASTIC AND ALL THINGS NEW. QUITE APPROPRIATE FOR YOU... MR. *MANDRAKE*.

HE DIDN'T ANSWER. HE WAS BOUNDING OUT TO LOOK AT THE VIEW.